D0545455

CONTENTS

MACHINES IN ACTION

These vehicles and machines are used for planting and harvesting crops on the farm.

Spreaders
These spread fertilizer over a field to help crops grow.

Find 3

Find 10

Tractors
A tractor is slow, but it can pull heavy machinery across a muddy field.

Four-wheel drive cars
Farmers need a vehicle they can drive over roads and rough tracks.

Find 3

Find 2

Seed drills
These plant seeds in tidy rows in the fields.

Find 6

Cats
Farm cats are very useful for catching mice.

Find 1
Round baler
This machine collects and packs cut straw, ready for collection.
Find 5
Wheelbarrows
A wheelbarrow is useful for moving heavy loads across the yard.
Find 2
Harrows
Harrows dig up fields, turning and loosening the soil.
Find 15
Cultivators
These get the soil ready for planting seeds.
Find 2
Bales
Straw is the stalks of crops like wheat and barley. It is gathered in bales.

COUNTING SHEEP

In early summer it's time to shear the sheep, so the shepherd leads her flock down from the hills.

Sheepdogs
Sheepdogs are trained to follow the shepherd's commands and herd the sheep.
Find 2
Find 1
Shepherd
The shepherd carries a stick called a crook to help guide the sheep.
Ewes
Female sheep are called ewes. Some breeds have horns.
Find 11
Find 4
Black sheep
Some sheep are born with black fleeces.
Find 3
Feeding troughs
As well as grass, ewes are given extra feed to help them produce milk.

Rams
Rams are adult male sheep. They have longer horns than the females.
Find 3
Find 5
Rabbits
The sheep share the fields with wild rabbits that also eat the grass.
Find 4
Young ewes
The younger female sheep have not grown their horns yet.
Find 9
Crows
Crows use wool from the sheep to help line their nests.
Find 8
Lambs
Playful lambs love leaping and running around in the fields.

BUSY BARN

The horses share their barn with other animals that like the comfort of a dry, straw bed.

Ponies
Ponies are small horses with thicker manes and coats.

Find 3

Horses
Every morning each horse is groomed and taken for a ride in the fields.

Find 4

Donkeys
Donkeys are related to horses. They are smaller, but very strong.

Find 3

Llamas
The woolly llama is a camel relative from South America that only eats plants.

Find 2

Barn owls and owlets
Owls often nest in old buildings. Their babies have soft, downy feathers.

Find 6

Find 5
Swallows
These fast-flying birds catch insects in the air to feed to their hungry young.
Find 7
Chickens
The chickens explore the cosy barn for beetles and other insects.
Find 7
Mice
The mice sneak into the barn to nibble on grain and the other animals' feed.
Find 3
Rats
The brown rat will eat almost anything. Birds must guard their eggs.
Find 3
Saddles
Putting a saddle on a horse makes riding more comfortable.

Sausages
Sausages are normally made from pork or beef.

Find 8

Find 7

Fried eggs
Eggs come from hens, ducks, and geese. Then they're cooked in the kitchen.

FRIENDLY FARMHOUSE

In the farmhouse kitchen, there are many things that started out in the farm fields.

Cheeses
Most cheese is made using milk taken from cows.

Find 7

Find 1

Butter
Butter is made from the fat in cow's cream or milk.

Find 5

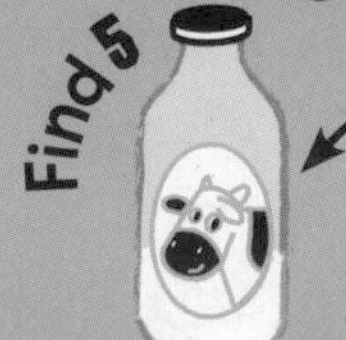

Bottles of milk
A cow's milk is usually collected twice a day.

Find 11
Pears
These pears were picked from trees in the orchard.
Find 2
Slices of bread
Bread is made using flour, which is formed by grinding crops like wheat or rye.
Find 9
Fruit preserves
These are made from fruit heated up with sugar. Delicious!
Find 9
Find 1
Sweater
The wool for this piece of clothing came from sheep.
Vegetables
Many of these vegetables were planted as crops in the fields.

Rabbits
The rabbits like company
and space to hop about.
Find 10
Guinea pigs
A guinea pig eats mostly
dried grass called hay.
Find 7
URBAN FARM
For children living in the city, an urban farm
is a great way to get close to animals.
Goats
Goats will eat almost anything, so
keep your snacks out of reach!
Find 6
Find 6
Piglets
Some piglets have escaped from their pen.
Can you spot where they've got to?
Find 6
Lambs
The lambs drink milk from
their mother, or from bottles.

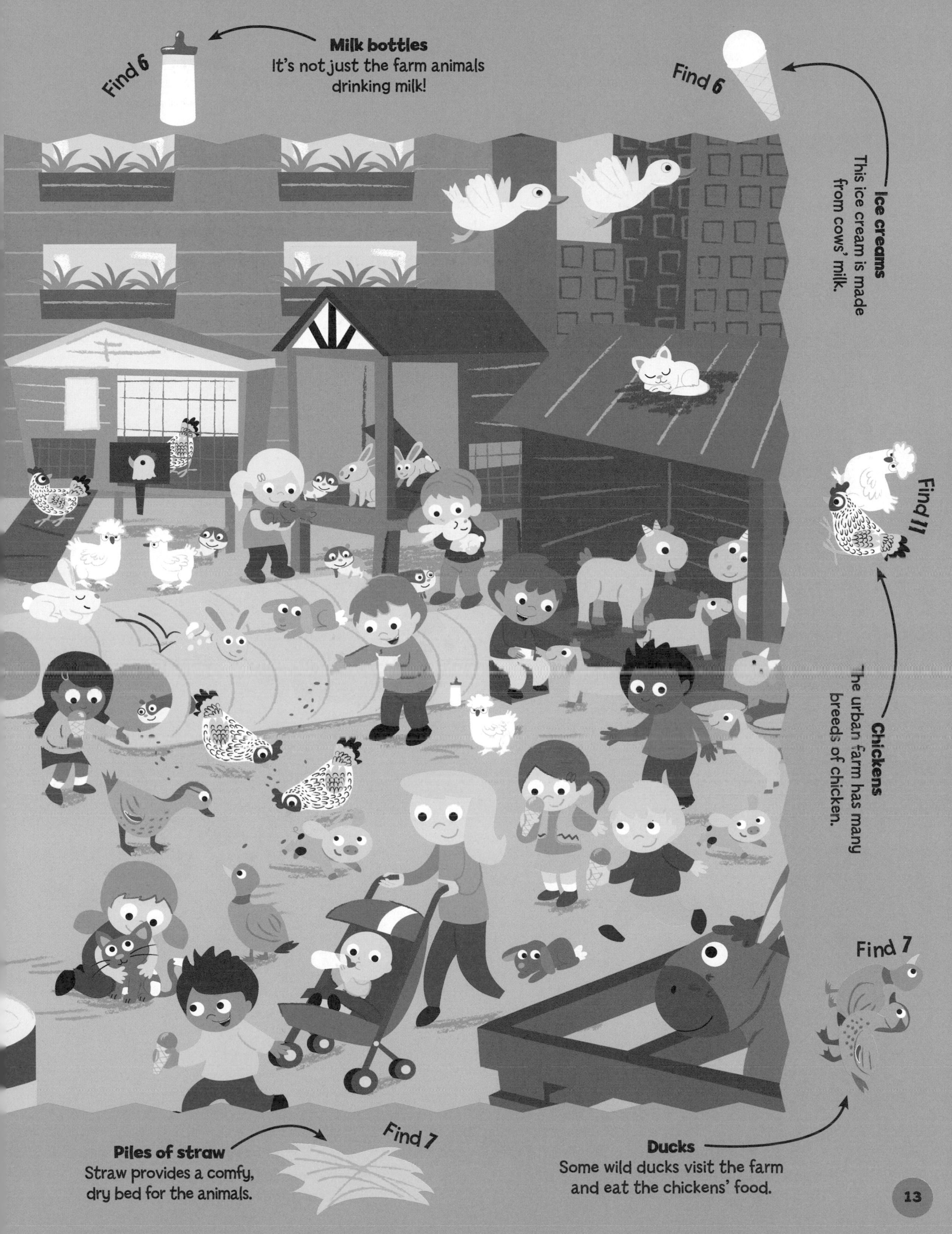

Find 6
Milk bottles
It's not just the farm animals drinking milk!
Find 6
Ice creams
This ice cream is made from cows' milk.
Find 11
Chickens
The urban farm has many breeds of chicken.
Find 7
Find 7
Piles of straw
Straw provides a comfy, dry bed for the animals.
Ducks
Some wild ducks visit the farm and eat the chickens' food.

BABY ANIMALS

Young animals on the farm need special attention in their first few months.

Ducklings
The mother duck tries to lead her ducklings to water.

Find 7

Piglets
Pigs have litters of about 10 piglets twice a year.

Find 3

Kittens
Baby cats drink their mother's milk and play fight with each other.

Find 3

Goslings
Young geese are called goslings. They have little, fluffy feathers.

Find 4

Lambs
Sheep can only feed two lambs. If a third is born, the farmer may need to care for it.

Find 3

Find 3
Kids
A baby goat is called a kid. It feeds on a nanny goat's milk.
Find 15
Chicks
Newly-hatched hen chicks are kept warm in pens before being set free to roam.
Find 5
Cygnets
Baby swans often sit under their mothers' wings to keep warm.
Find 3
Foals
A baby horse can be up and walking just minutes after being born.
Find 6
Calves
A young cow stays with its mother for eight months after it is born.

AFTER DARK

On a cold winter's morning, the farmer has to get up before sunrise to check on the animals.

Foxes
The foxes hunt mostly at night for wild rabbits and birds.

Find 2

Find 4

Hedgehogs
It's almost the time of the year for the hedgehogs to hibernate.

Pigs
The pigs keep snug in a pile of dry straw.

Find 16

Find 6

Cows
The cows stay in a shed, where they are fed damp grass called silage.

Find 5

Badgers
Wild badgers often come sniffing for leftover animal feed.

Tawny owls
The owl hunts for mice
and voles at night.
Find 2
Find 7
Sheep
With thick fleeces, the sheep can
keep warm, even when it snows.
Find 1
Farmer
A farmer leaves the house at half past
five in the morning to milk the cows.
Find 2
Bats
Tiny bats can catch small
insects while they are flying.
Find 6
Horses
Horses keep warm in winter
by wearing blankets.

POND SPLASHING

The pond is home to farm ducks and geese, as well as some wild visitors!

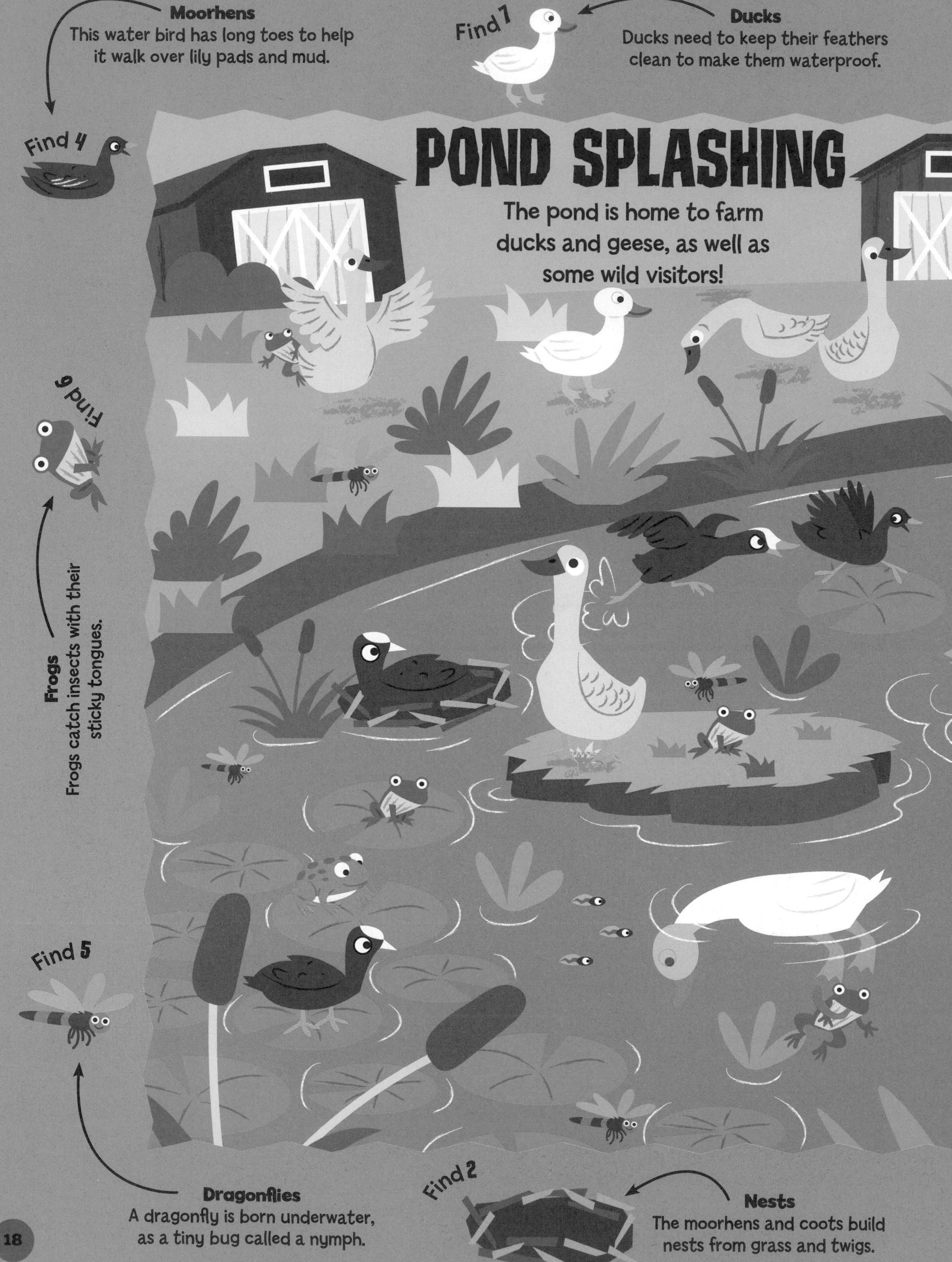

Moorhens
This water bird has long toes to help it walk over lily pads and mud.
Find 4
Find 7
Ducks
Ducks need to keep their feathers clean to make them waterproof.
Find 9
Frogs
Frogs catch insects with their sticky tongues.
Find 5
Dragonflies
A dragonfly is born underwater, as a tiny bug called a nymph.
Find 2
Nests
The moorhens and coots build nests from grass and twigs.

Toads
Toads are larger than frogs and have more warts.
Find 2
Find 5
Coots
Coots do not like other water birds near their nests.
Find 6
Geese
Geese eat mostly grass and make lots of honking noises.
Find 13
Grey heron
This tall bird stands very still, waiting to catch a fish or frog.
Find 1
Tadpoles
Tadpoles are young frogs that have left their eggs (which are called frogspawn).

ROUNDUP!

On this ranch, it's time for the cattle to get their regular health checks. But first they need to be rounded up!

Cattle
The cows spend most of the year grazing in open fields.

Find 17

Windmills
Windmills are used to pump water from underground.

Find 3

Calves
New calves in the herd need to be counted.

Find 9

Find 10

Cowgirls and cowboys
All the herders are expert horseriders with amazing rope skills.

Lassos
Cow herders throw this loop of rope to catch cattle by the horns.

Find 7

Find 8
Horses
A horse is the best way to travel over the wild lands where the cattle graze.
Find 10
Cowboy hats
Cowboys wear a wide-brimmed hat to keep the sun off their faces and necks.
Find 4
Coyotes
Small wolves called coyotes are kept away by the herders.
Find 4
Rattlesnakes
Watch where you step! This snake has a venomous bite.
Find 2
Ranch houses
Ranch houses are normally on one level, rather than having stairs.

FLYING FRIENDS

The free-range farm looks after lots of birds, and not just chickens!

Turkeys
Turkeys like treats, such as apples, plums, and sweetcorn.

Find 10

Find 1

Rooster
The male chicken wakes up the farm with a "cock-a-doodle-doo!"

Quails
A quail is half the size of a chicken, and lays tiny eggs.

Find 5

Find 10

Eggs
Eggs are collected twice each day.

Find 6

Guinea fowl
If these birds see a stranger or a fox, they will make lots of noise!

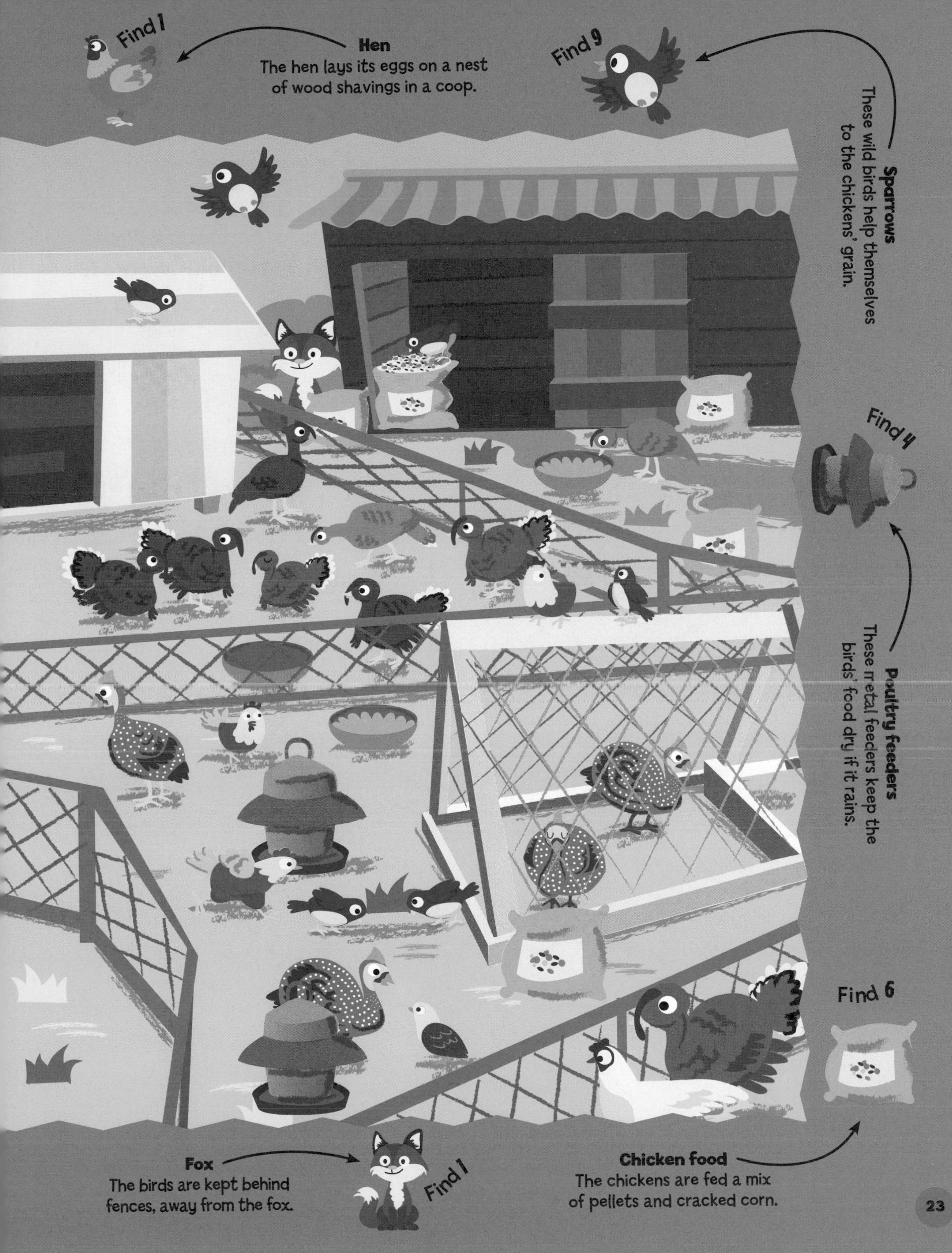

Find 1
Hen
The hen lays its eggs on a nest of wood shavings in a coop.
Find 9
Sparrows
These wild birds help themselves to the chickens' grain.
Find 4
Poultry feeders
These metal feeders keep the birds' food dry if it rains.
Find 6
Fox
The birds are kept behind fences, away from the fox.
Find 1
Chicken food
The chickens are fed a mix of pellets and cracked corn.

THE HARVEST

The vegetables are ready for harvesting. What delicious things have been dug up and collected?

Beans
Beans grow on vines. The vines climb up wooden canes.

Find 13

Find 1

Scarecrow
The scarecrow is meant to keep birds away from the seeds and crops.

Beets
Both the leaves and the red root on the beet can be eaten.

Find 18

Find 22

Potatoes
The potato was first grown as food in South America 7,000 years ago.

Find 2

Compost heaps
Rotting plants become compost that can add goodness to the soil.

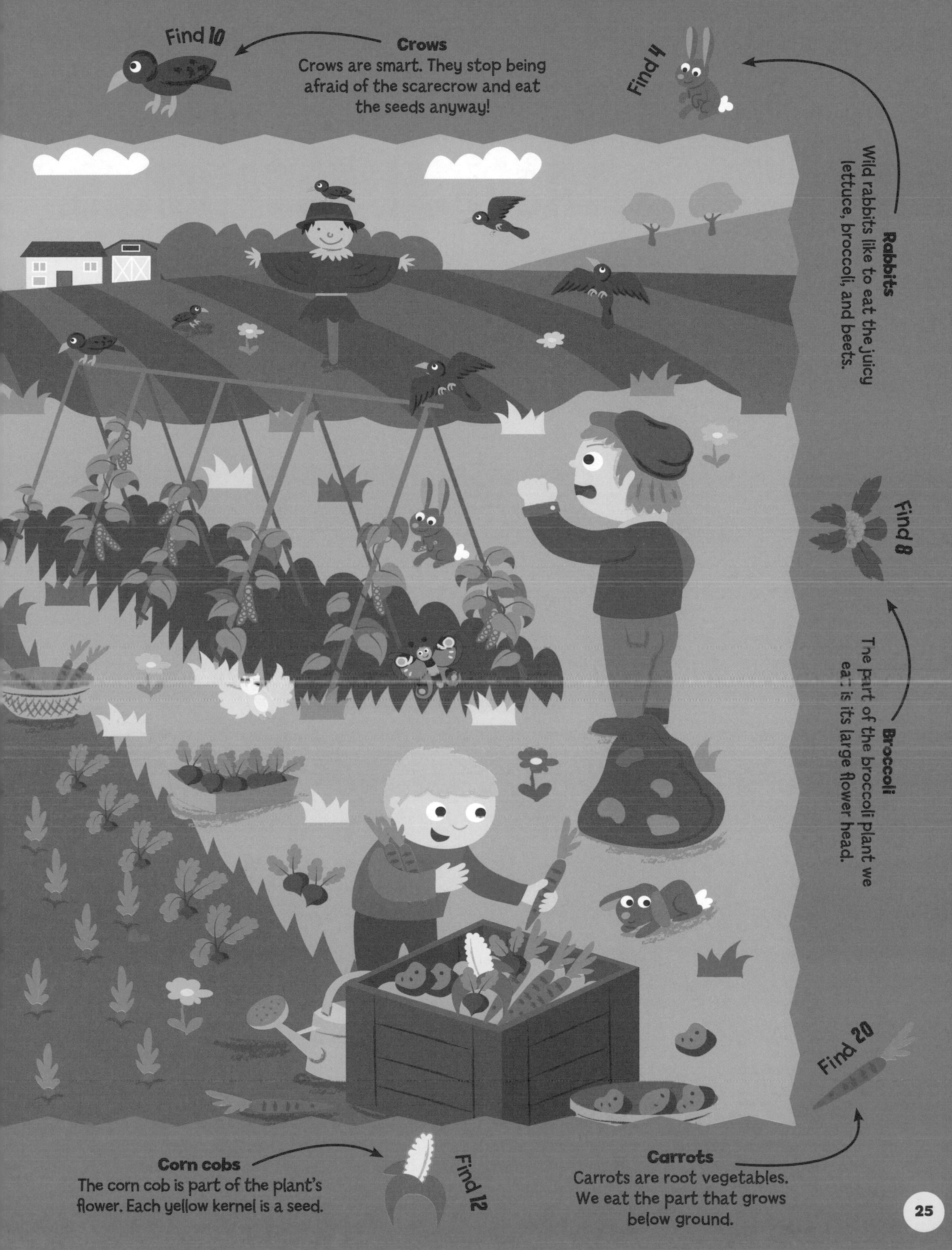
Crows
Crows are smart. They stop being afraid of the scarecrow and eat the seeds anyway!
Find 10
Find 4
Rabbits
Wild rabbits like to eat the juicy lettuce, broccoli, and beets.
Find 8
Broccoli
The part of the broccoli plant we eat is its large flower head.
Find 20
Corn cobs
The corn cob is part of the plant's flower. Each yellow kernel is a seed.
Find 12
Carrots
Carrots are root vegetables. We eat the part that grows below ground.

TROPICAL TREASURES

On the tropical farm, exotic fruits are being grown. How many of these have you tasted?

Custard apples
These bumpy fruits are soft and white on the inside, with large seeds.

Find 9

Find 7

Banana bunches
Bananas grow in large bunches. They turn from green to yellow as they ripen.

Durians
This fruit is tasty, but is one of the smelliest in the world!

Find 4

Find 8

Pineapples
One pineapple can take two years to grow.

Find 8

Rambutans
Inside the prickly, red skin is a soft, white fruit and a big seed.

Find 8
Dragon fruit
This bright pink fruit grows on a large cactus.
Find 2
Watermelon slices
The large, juicy watermelon grows on the ground on a vine.
Find 12
Mangos
Mango trees can live for hundreds of years.
Find 19
Guavas
Guavas can be large and crunchy or small, soft, and sweet.
Find 15
Avocados
The skin of an avocado can be green or black, depending on which type it is.

RICE PADDY

Rice is a kind of seed that is eaten around the world. It is grown in a flooded field called a paddy.

Rice farmers
Rice seedlings are hand-planted in flooded fields.

Find 14

Water buffalo
Buffalo help to pull carts in the fields.

Find 6

Planting machine
Nowadays, some farmers use machines to plant rice.

Find 1

Find 2

Cultivators
These machines turn the soil to bring nutrients to the surface.

Find 3

Yokes
Workers use poles to balance baskets of rice on their shoulders.

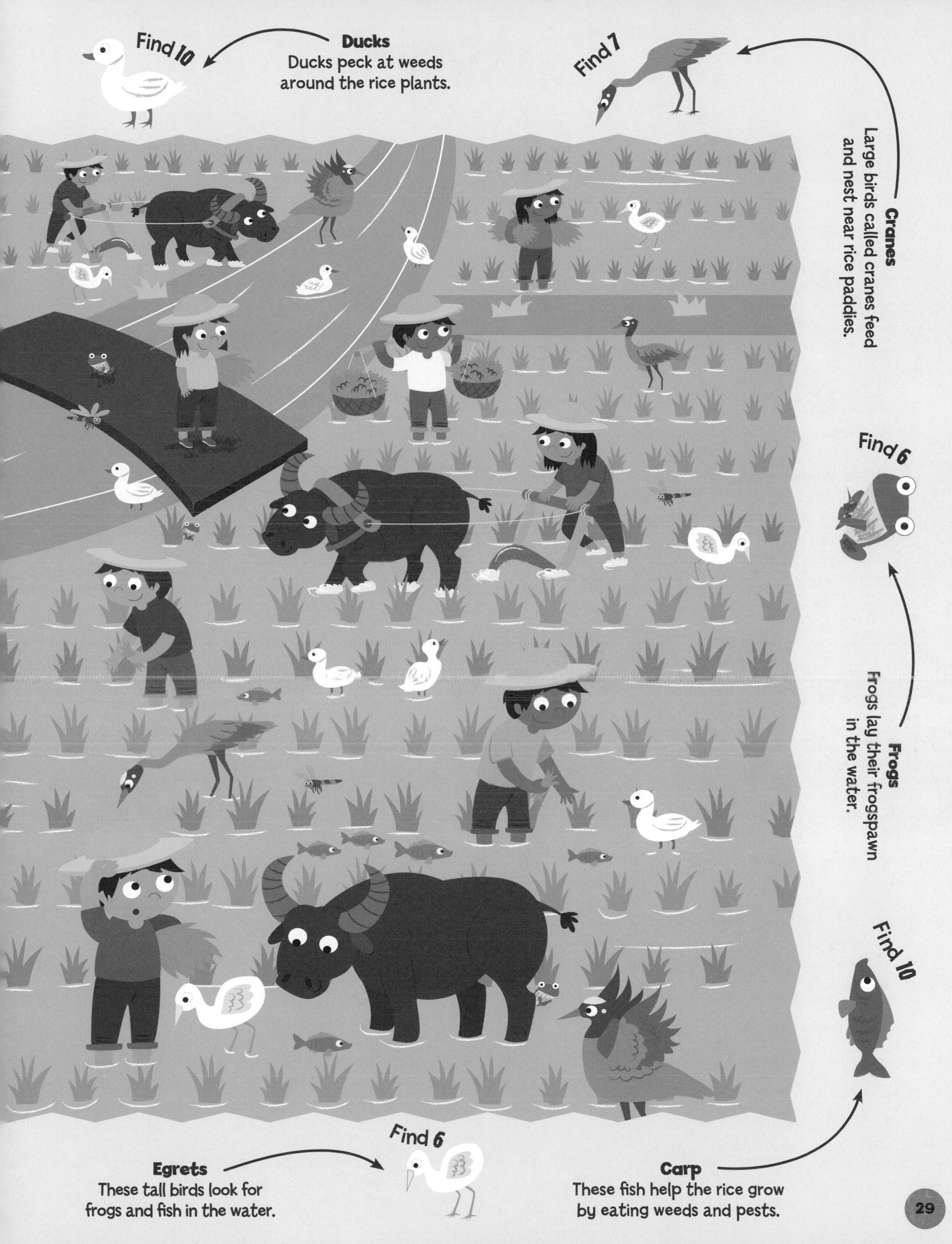
Find 10
Ducks
Ducks peck at weeds around the rice plants.
Find 7
Cranes
Large birds called cranes feed and nest near rice paddies.
Find 6
Frogs
Frogs lay their frogspawn in the water.
Find 10
Find 6
Egrets
These tall birds look for frogs and fish in the water.
Carp
These fish help the rice grow by eating weeds and pests.

Answers

4–5 MACHINES IN ACTION

- Tractors
- Spreaders
- Four-wheel drive cars
- Seed drills
- Cats
- Cultivators
- Bales
- Harrows
- Wheelbarrows
- Round baler

6–7 COUNTING SHEEP

- Shepherd
- Sheepdogs
- Ewes
- Black sheep
- Feeding troughs
- Crows
- Lambs
- Young ewes
- Rabbits
- Rams

8–9 BUSY BARN

- Horses
- Ponies
- Donkeys
- Llamas
- Barn owls and owlets
- Saddles
- Rats
- Mice
- Chickens
- Swallows

10-11 FRIENDLY FARMHOUSE

- Fried eggs
- Sausages
- Cheeses
- Butter
- Bottles of milk
- Sweater
- Vegetables
- Fruit preserves
- Slices of bread
- Pears

12—13 URBAN FARM

- Guinea pigs
- Rabbits
- Goats
- Piglets
- Lambs
- Piles of straw
- Ducks
- Chickens
- Ice creams
- Milk bottles

14-15 BABY ANIMALS

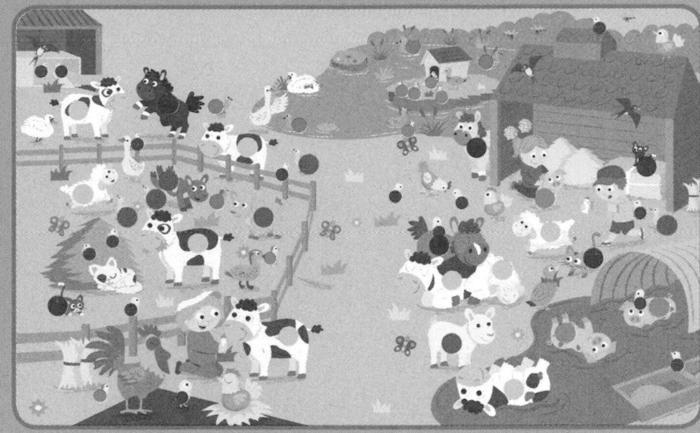

- Ducklings
- Piglets
- Kittens
- Goslings
- Lambs
- Calves
- Foals
- Cygnets
- Chicks
- Kids

16 17 AFTER DARK

- Hedgehogs
- Foxes
- Pigs
- Cows
- Badgers
- Bats
- Horses
- Farmer
- Sheep
- Tawny owls

18 19 POND SPLASHING

- Ducks
- Moorhens
- Frogs
- Dragonflies
- Nests
- Grey heron
- Tadpoles
- Geese
- Coots
- Toads

20-21 ROUNDUP!

- Windmills
- Cattle
- Calves
- Cowgirls and cowboys
- Lassos
- Ranch houses
- Rattlesnakes
- Coyotes
- Cowboy hats
- Horses

22–23 FLYING FRIENDS

- Rooster
- Turkeys
- Quails
- Eggs
- Guinea fowl
- Fox
- Chicken food
- Poultry feeders
- Sparrows
- Hen

24-25 THE HARVEST

- Scarecrow
- Beans
- Beets
- Potatoes
- Compost heaps
- Corn cobs
- Carrots
- Broccoli
- Rabbits
- Crows

26-27 TROPICAL TREASURES

- Banana bunches
- Custard apples
- Durians
- Pineapples
- Rambutans
- Guavas
- Avocados
- Mangos
- Watermelon slices
- Dragon fruit

28–29 RICE PADDY

- Water buffalo
- Rice farmers
- Planting machine
- Cultivators
- Yokes
- Egrets
- Carp
- Frogs
- Cranes
- Ducks